Canada's #1 Educational Resource

Reading · Math · More

Workbook

Pre K

Canadian Curriculum Press
Forward Learning

Table of Contents

Letter to Parents 1
All about Me 2
I Know My Colours! 3
Comparisons 4
What Comes Next? 5
Shapes 6
Hooray for Patterns 7
Colour Patterns 8
Pencil Pals 9
Learning about Letters 15
Letter Practice 28
I Know My Letters 32
Nice Numbers 1 to 10 33
Hooray for Counting 38
More and Less 40
Weather and Seasons 41

by
Margaret Ann Hawkins

Editors
Lisa Penttilä
Vin Sriniketh

Layout & Design
Michael P. Brodey

Canadian Curriculum Press
is an imprint of Telegraph Road
12 Cranfield Road,
Toronto, Ontario, Canada
M4B 3G8

©2017 Telegraph Road Entertainment
ALL RIGHTS RESERVED
ISBN 978-1-4876-0158-4

For special bulk purchases, please contact:
sales@telegraph-rd.com

For other inquiries, please contact:
inquiries@telegraph-rd.com

Printed in China

Dear Parents,

This Canadian Pre-Kindergarten workbook contains colourful activities that will keep your child absorbed and learning while at home or on the go! Each activity is designed to focus on key skills he or she will use at school: identifying letters, numbers, and colours; sorting and comparing; making patterns; developing eye-hand coordination and fine motor control; and more!

Enjoy this learning time with your child. Your encouragement will help your child build the skills and confidence needed for success in Kindergarten and beyond!

Sincerely,

The Canadian Curriculum Press team

S0-CBM-529

We acknowledge the financial support of the Government of Canada through the Canada Book Fund (CBF) for our publishing activities.

  Canadian Heritage Patrimoine canadien   Canada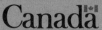

All about Me

This is me!

This is where I live!

Trace and colour.

I am _____ years old.

I live in Canada.

2

I Know My Colours!

Colour the can to match the spilled paint. Trace the colour word. Say the colour name.

red

blue

orange

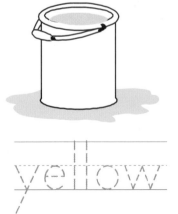
yellow

green

pink

Match the picture to the colour word. One is done.

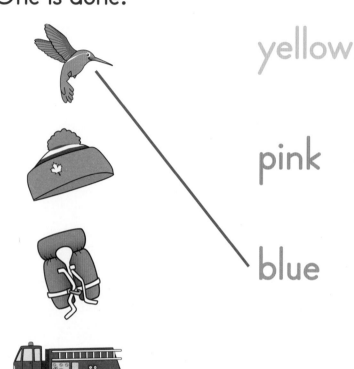

yellow

pink

blue

green

orange

red

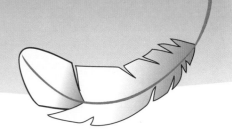

Comparisons

Heavy or Light?
Colour heavy things green.
Colour light things red.

Capacity
Circle the one that holds more.
Make an X on the one that holds less.

4

Draw the missing picture.

 _____

Draw the missing picture.

  _____

Print the missing numbers.

1 2 __ 4 5 __

Look at the mixed up pictures below. Use numbers 1 2 3 4 to put pictures in the correct order. The first one has been started for you.

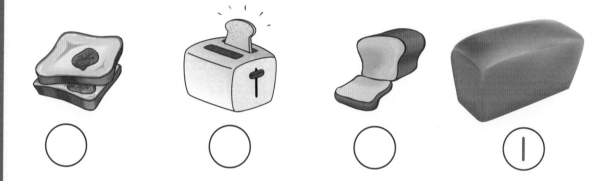

◯   ◯   ◯   ①

◯   ◯

◯   ◯

SHAPES

Trace each shape with your finger. Say each name.

circle square triangle rectangle

Trace the shapes. Draw the shape on the line.

square

triangle

circle

rectangle

Colour the shape that matches the first one.

circle

square

triangle

rectangle

A pattern repeats over and over. Look at this pattern. Say the name of each shape.

Say the names of the things in each pattern. Circle what comes next.

Action Patterns
Make these patterns by clapping 🖐 and stomping 👟.

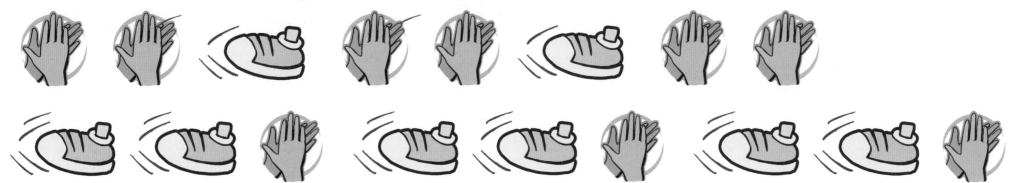

Try making different action patterns with your hands and feet. Say the actions in your patterns.

Colour Patterns

Use red , yellow  and blue  to continue the pattern. Say the colours.

R   Y   B   ___ ___ ___ ___ ___ ___ ___

Colour the pictures to make a pattern. Tell what pattern you made.

Trace the tree trunk. Start at the red dot.

Trace the branches. Start at the red dot.

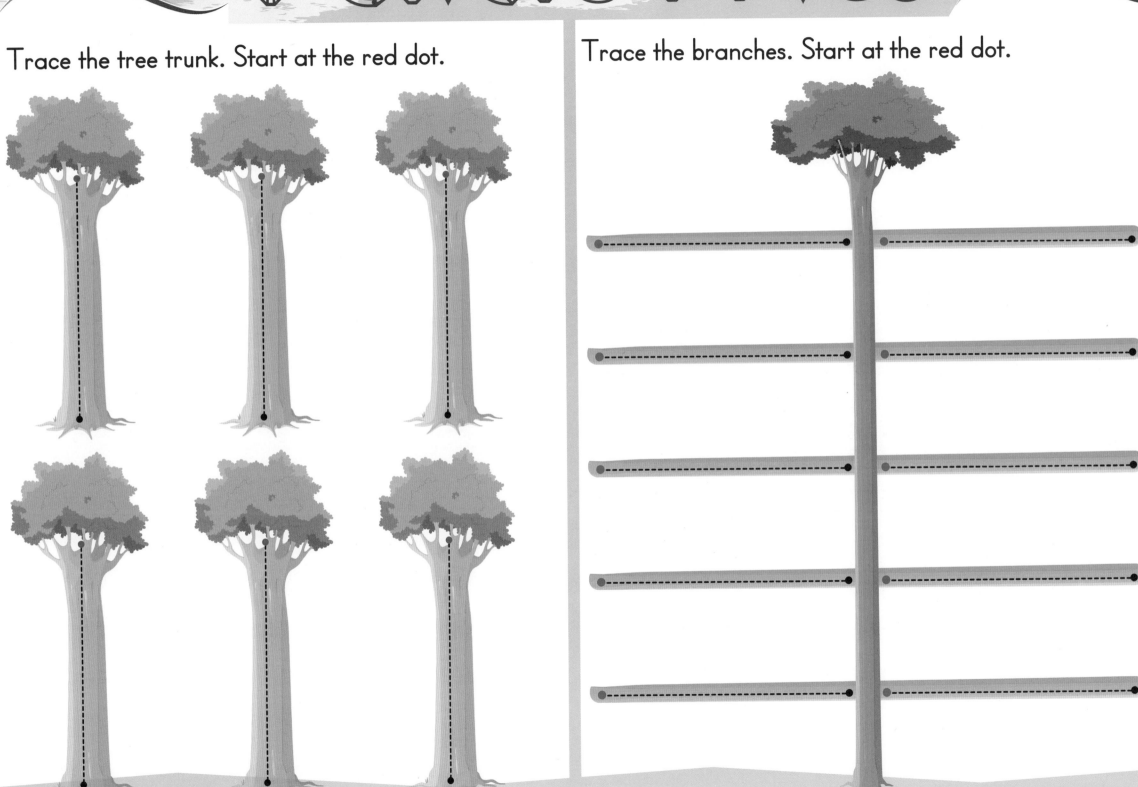

9

Trace the mountains. Start at the red dot.

Trace the pattern on the sweater. Start at the red dot.

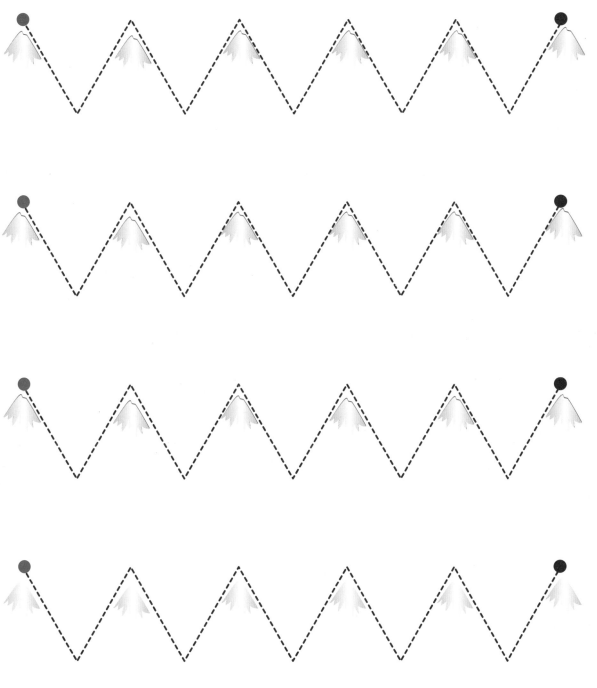

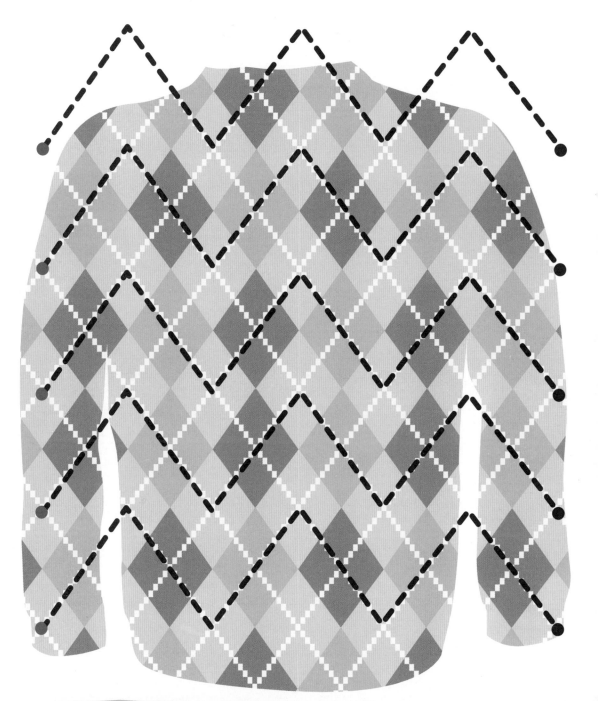

PENCIL PALS

Trace the beach balls. Start at the red dot. Follow the arrow.　Trace the bubbles. Start at the red dot. Follow the arrow.

Trace the elephant ears. Start at the red dot.

Trace the sippy cup handles. Start at the red dot.

Trace the snakes. Start at the red dot.

Trace the waves. Start at the red dot.

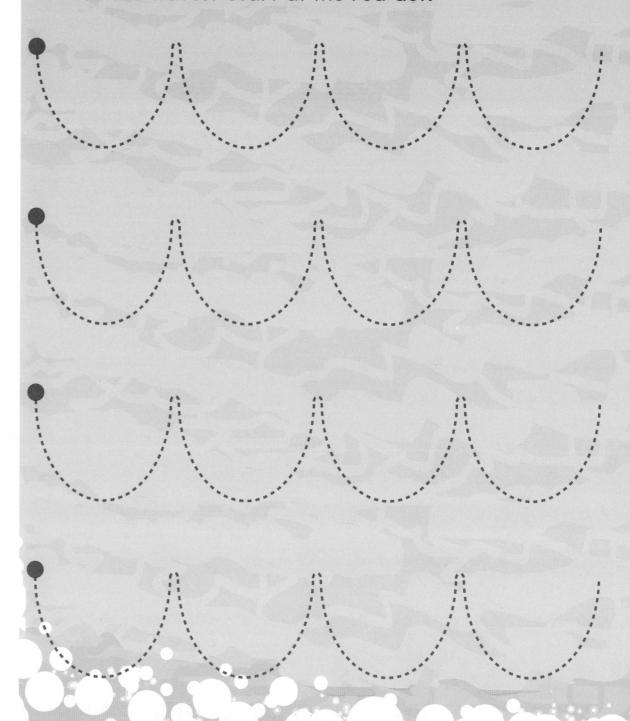

PENCIL PALS

Trace the anthills. Start at the red dot.

Trace the umbrellas. Start at the red dot.

Trace A and a. Say the letter sound.

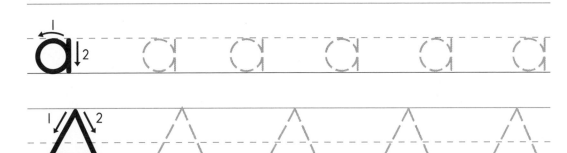

Follow the arrows with your finger, then a pencil.

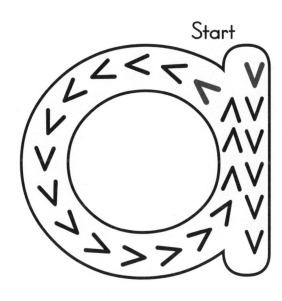

Start

Circle things that start with a. Say their names.

   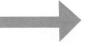

Trace B and b. Say the letter sound.

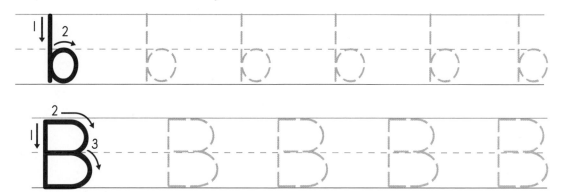

Follow the arrows with your finger, then a pencil.

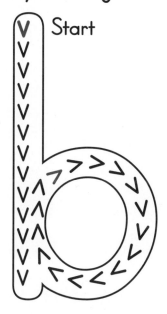

Start

Circle things that start with b. Say their names.

Trace c and C. Say the letter sound.

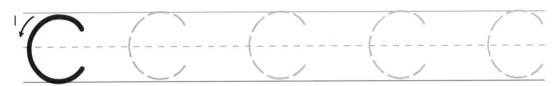

Follow the arrows with your finger, then a pencil.

Start

Circle things that start with c. Say their names.

Trace d and D . Say the letter sound.

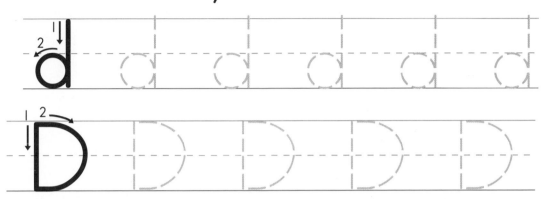

Follow the arrows with your finger, then a pencil.

Start

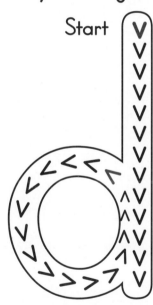

Circle things that start with d. Say their names.

Trace e and E. Say the letter sound.

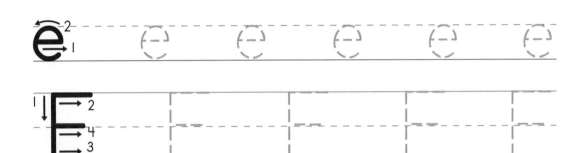

Trace f and F . Say the letter sound.

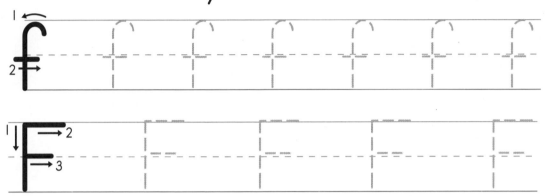

Follow the arrows with your finger, then a pencil.

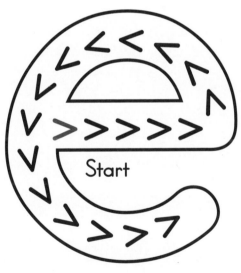

Start

Follow the arrows with your finger, then a pencil.

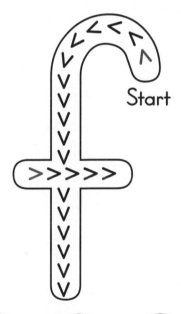

Start

Circle things that start with e. Say their names.

Circle things that start with f. Say their names.

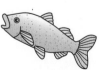 

Trace g and G. Say the letter sound.

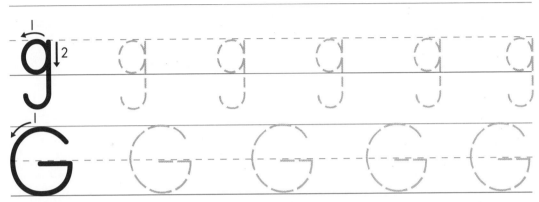

Follow the arrows with your finger, then a pencil.

Start

Circle things that start with g. Say their names.

Trace h and H. Say the letter sound.

Follow the arrows with your finger, then a pencil.

Start

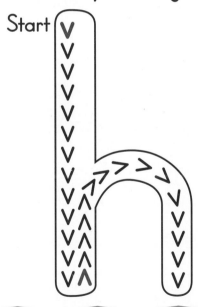

Circle things that start with h. Say their names.

Trace i and I. Say the letter sound.

Follow the arrows with your finger, then a pencil.

Start

Trace j and J. Say the letter sound.

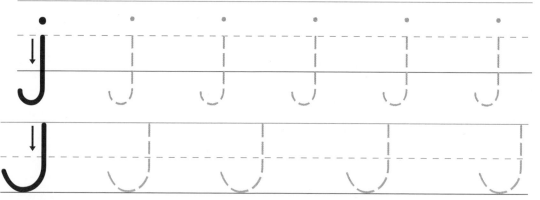

Follow the arrows with your finger, then a pencil.

Start

Circle things that start with i. Say their names.

Circle things that start with j. Say their names.

Trace k and K. Say the letter sound.

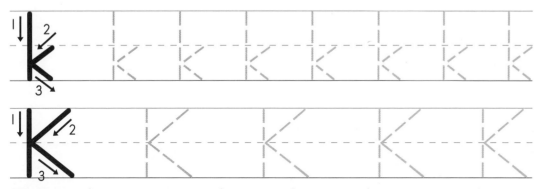

Follow the arrows with your finger, then a pencil.

Trace l and L . Say the letter sound.

Follow the arrows with your finger, then a pencil.

Start

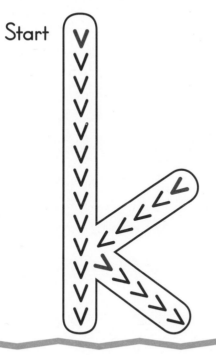

Start

Circle things that start with k. Say their names.

Circle things that start with l. Say their names.

Trace m and M. Say the letter sound.

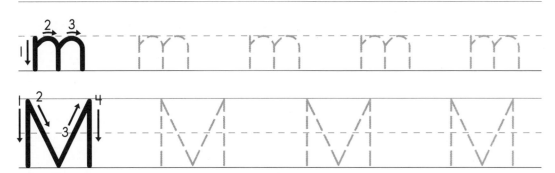

Follow the arrows with your finger, then a pencil.

Start

Monkey starts with the letter m.
Draw something else that starts with m.

Trace n and N . Say the letter sound.

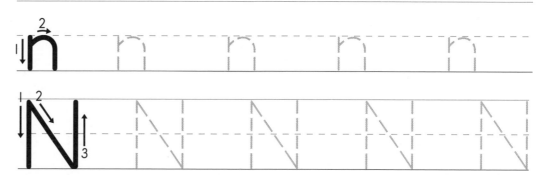

Follow the arrows with your finger, then a pencil.

Start

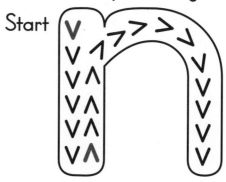

Nine starts with the letter n.
Draw something else that starts with n.

oO pP

Trace o and O. Say the letter sound.

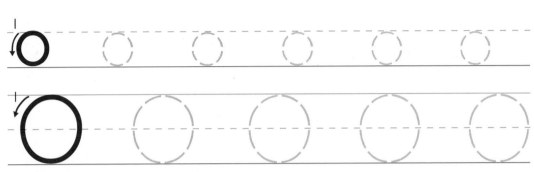

Follow the arrows with your finger, then a pencil.

Trace p and P. Say the letter sound.

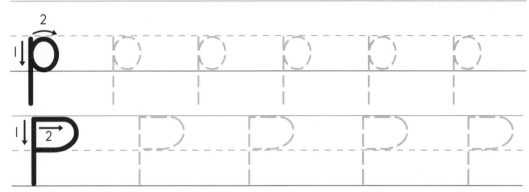

Follow the arrows with your finger, then a pencil.

Start

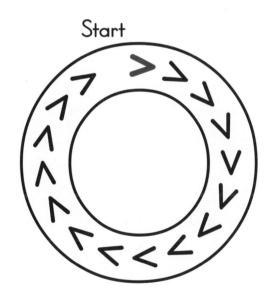

Start

Circle things that start with o. Say their names.

Circle things that start with p. Say their names.

Trace q and Q. Say the letter sound.

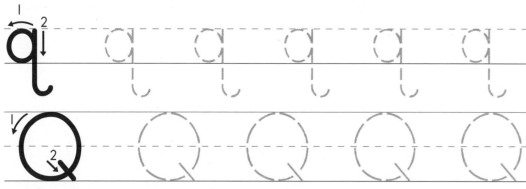

Follow the arrows with your finger, then a pencil.

Trace r and R . Say the letter sound.

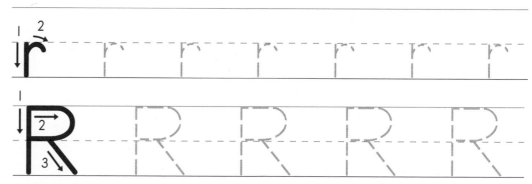

Follow the arrows with your finger, then a pencil.

Start

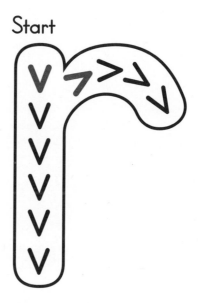

Start

Circle things that start with q. Say their names.

Circle things that start with r. Say their names.

Trace s and S. Say the letter sound.

s s s s s s s

S S S S S S

Follow the arrows with your finger, then a pencil.

 Start

Trace t and T. Say the letter sound.

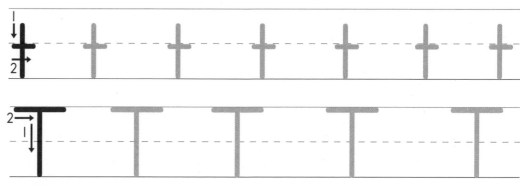

Follow the arrows with your finger, then a pencil.

Start

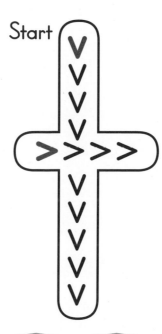

Circle things that start with s. Say their names.

Circle things that start with t. Say their names.

uU

uU

Trace u and U. Say the letter sound.

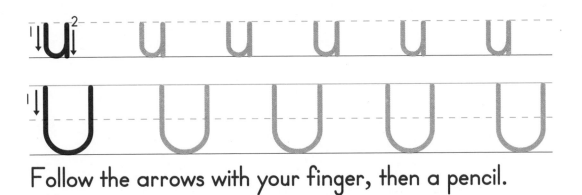

Follow the arrows with your finger, then a pencil.

Start

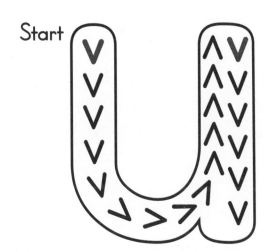

Circle things that start with u. Say their names.

UP

vV

Trace v and V . Say the letter sound.

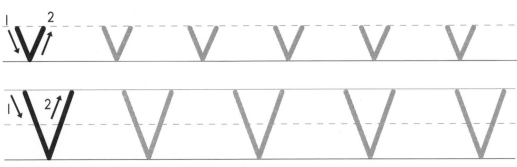

Follow the arrows with your finger, then a pencil.

Start

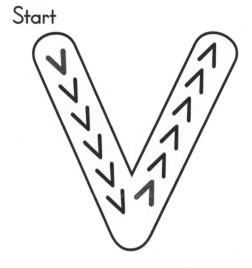

Circle things that start with v. Say their names.

25

Trace w and W. Say the letter sound.

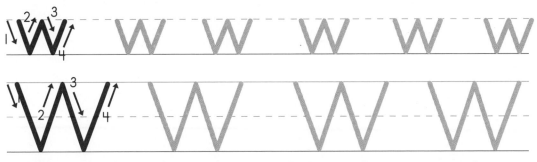

Follow the arrows with your finger, then a pencil.

Trace x and X . Say the letter sound.

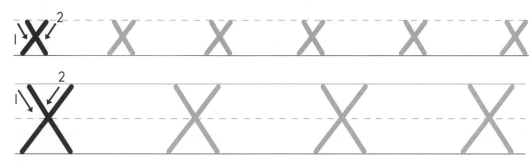

Follow the arrows with your finger, then a pencil.

Start

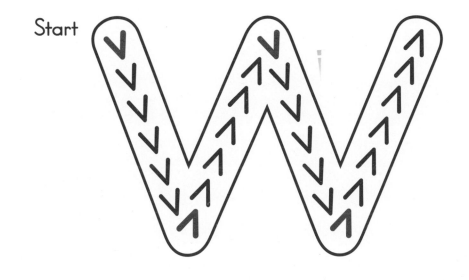

Start

Circle things that start with w. Say their names.

Circle things that start or end with x. Say their names.

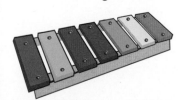

y Y

z Z

Trace y and Y. Say the letter sound.

Follow the arrows with your finger, then a pencil.

Trace z and Z . Say the letter sound.

Follow the arrows with your finger, then a pencil.

Start

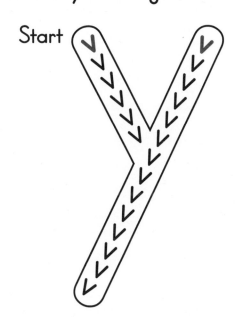

Start

Circle things that start with y. Say their names.

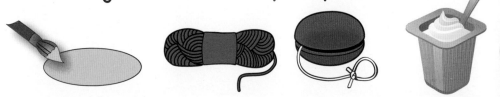

Circle things that start with z. Say their names.

Letter Practice

Letters with Straight Lines
Trace the letters.

E   E   E   E

F   F   F   F

H   H   H   H

Ii   Ii   Ii   Ii

Ll   Ll   Ll   Ll

Tt   Tt   Tt   Tt

Letters with Slanted Lines
Trace the letters.

A   A   A   A   A   A

K   k   K   k   K   k

M   M   M   M   M

N   N   N   N   N

V   v   V   v   V   v

W   w   W   w   W   w

X   x   X   x   X   x

Y   y   Y   y   Y   y

Z   z   Z   z   Z   z

Letter Practice

Letters with Curvy Lines

Trace the letters.

a a a a a   G g G g G g

B b B b B b   h h h h h h

C c C c C c   J j J j J j

D d D d D d   m m m m m m

e e e e e e   n n n n n n

f f f f f f   O o O o O o

Letter Practice

Trace the red path from Aa to Zz.

Start

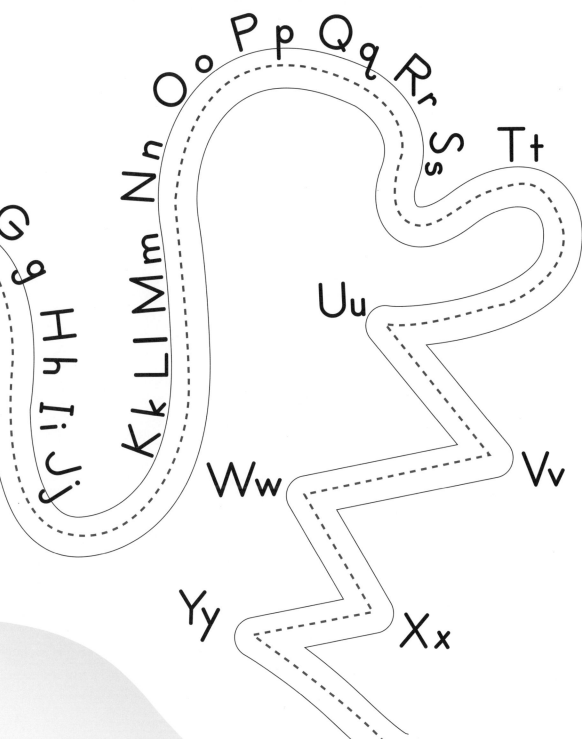

Aa Bb Cc Dd Ee Ff Gg Hh Ii Jj Kk Ll Mm Nn Oo Pp Qq Rr Ss Tt Uu Vv Ww Xx Yy Zz

More Letters with Curvy Lines

Trace the letters.

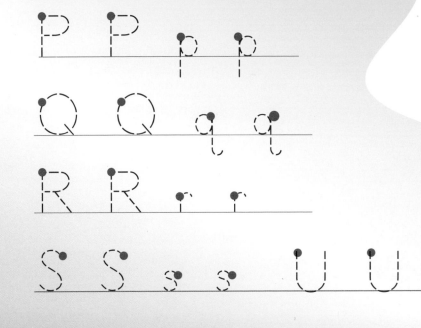

P P p p

Q Q q q

R R r r

S S s s U U u u

Letter Practice

Join the dots from Aa to Zz. Colour the balloons your favourite colour.

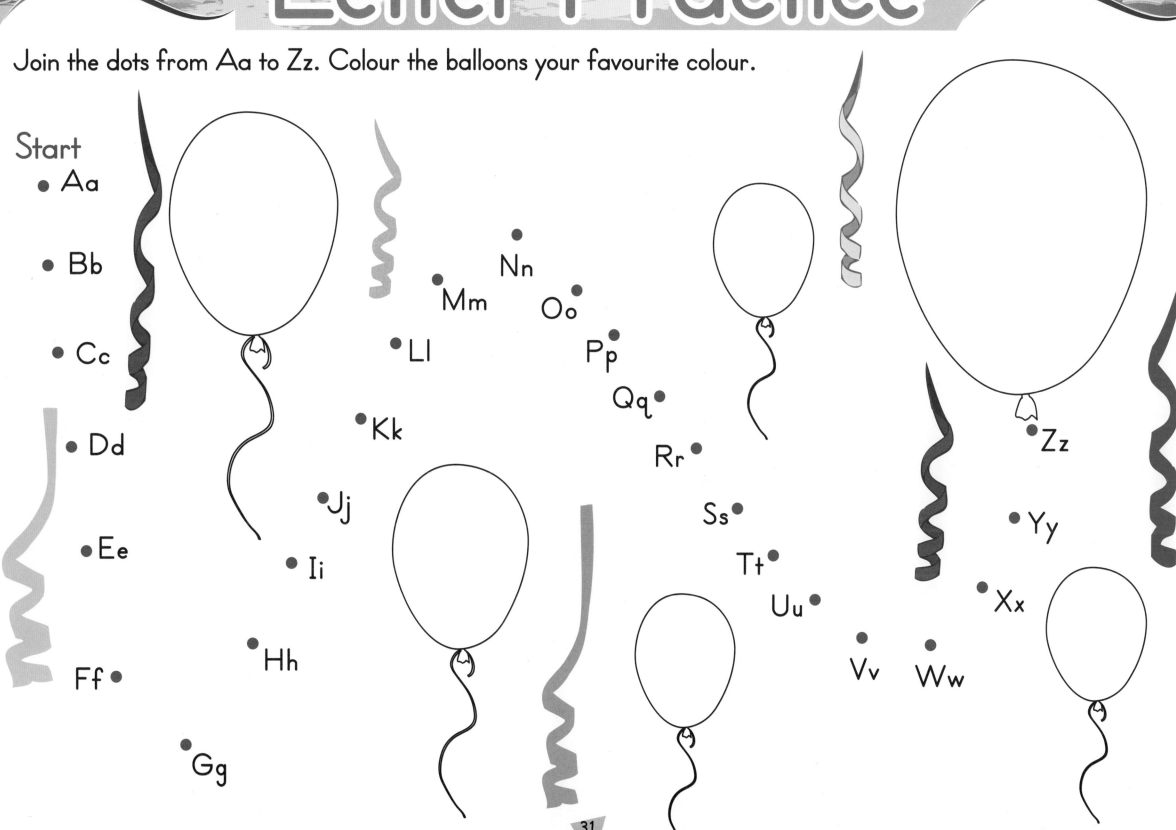

Start
- Aa
- Bb
- Cc
- Dd
- Ee
- Ff

Gg

Hh

Ii

Jj

Kk

Ll

Mm

Nn

Oo

Pp

Qq

Rr

Ss

Tt

Uu

Vv

Ww

Xx

Yy

Zz

I Know My Letters!

a b c d e f g h i j k l m n o p q r s t u v w x y z

Draw a line from the item to the letter it starts with. The first one is done for you.

Draw a line from the letter to the item that starts with that sound. The first one is done for you.

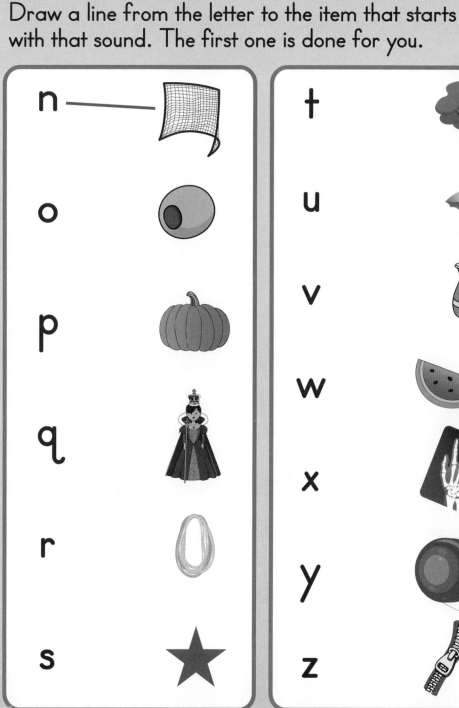

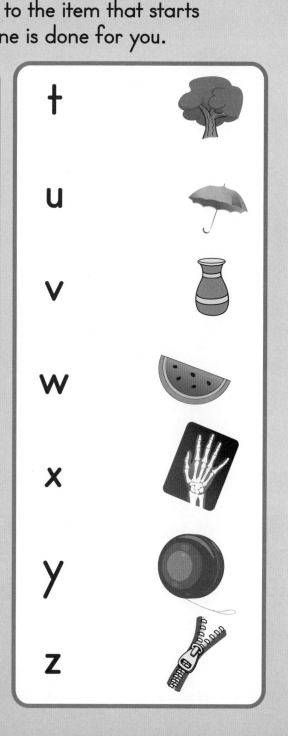

Trace the number 1.

Trace the number 2.

Colour the cow.

How many cows do you see? _____

Count the chickens.

How many do you see? _____

Trace the number 3.

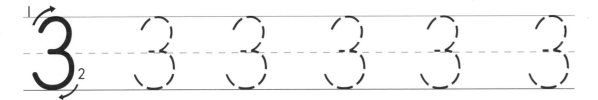

Trace the number 4.

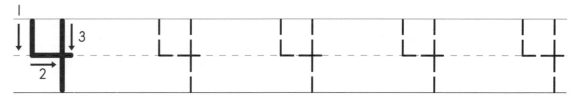

Colour the pigs.

How many do you see? ____

Count the goats.

How many do you see? ____

Trace the number 5.

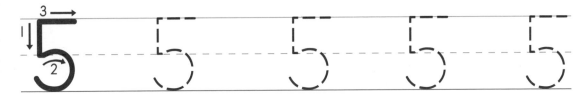

Trace the number 6.

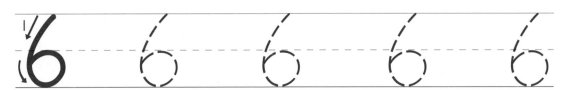

Colour the snowy owls.

How many do you see? _____

Count the bulls.

How many do you see? _____

Trace the number 7.

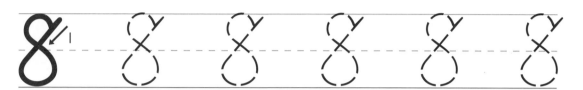

Trace the number 8.

Colour the ladybugs.

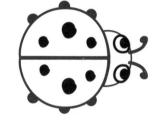 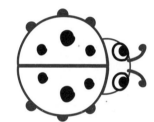 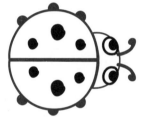

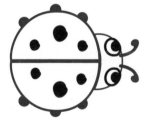 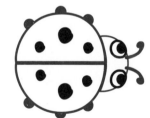 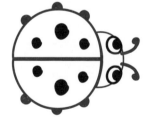

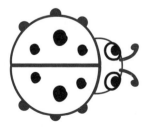

How many do you see? _____

Count the dragonflies.

How many do you see? _____

Trace the number 9.

Trace the number 10.

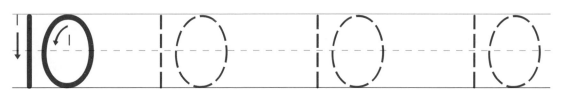

Colour the bees.

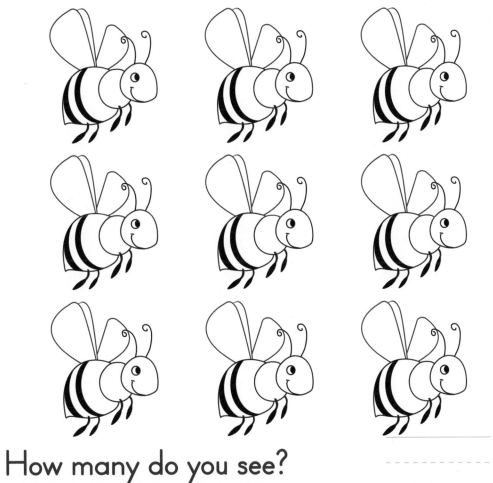

How many do you see? _____

Count the fish.

How many do you see? _____

Hooray for Counting!

How many? Count aloud. Circle the number.

 1

 1 2

 1 2 3

 1 2 3 4

1 2 3 4 5

Look at the number. Draw a line to the matching picture.

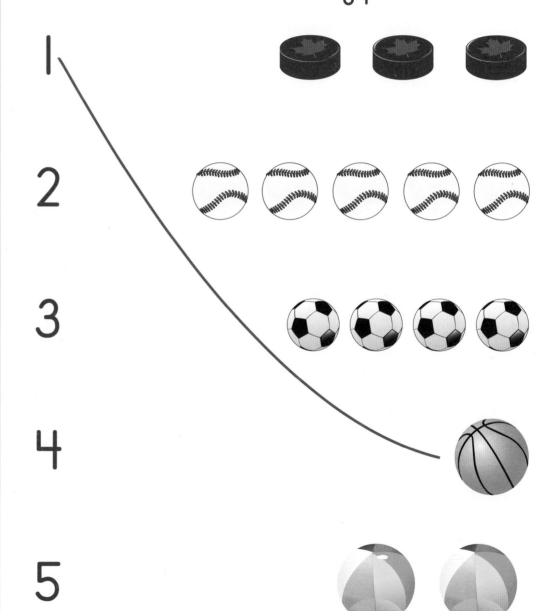

1

2

3

4

5

How many? Count aloud. Circle the number.

6

6 7

6 7 8

6 7 8 9

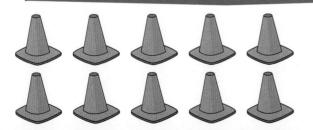

6 7 8 9 10

Look at the number. Draw a line to the matching picture.

6

7

8

9

10

Count. Circle the group that has more.

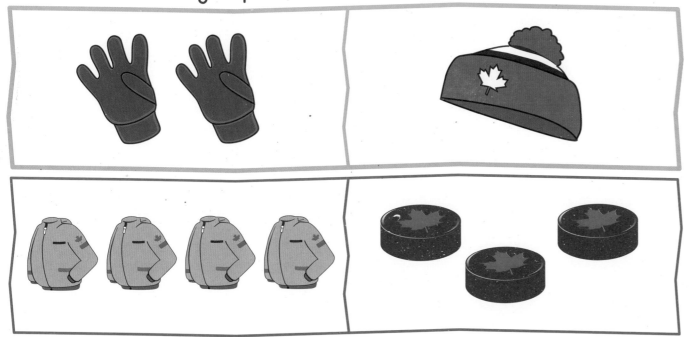

Follow the instructions to finish each picture.

Draw 3 fish in the fishbowl.

Count. Circle the group that has fewer.

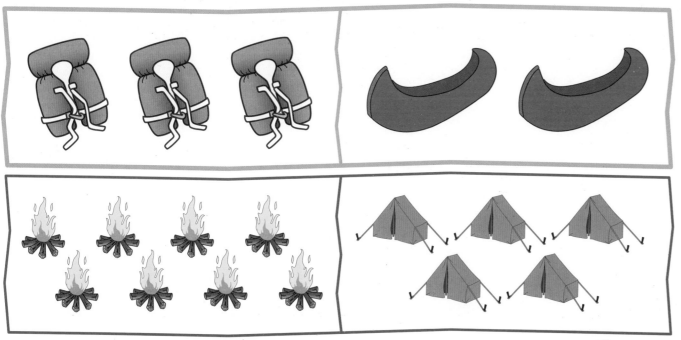

Draw 5 pears on the tree.